# Transfer Window

Tales of the Mistakes of the Healthy

Published by Nordisk Books, 2019
www.nordiskbooks.com

Translated from *Transfervindue*, copyright © Maria Gerhardt & JP/
Politikens Hus A/S 2017 in agreement with Politiken Literary Agency

This translation has been published with the financial support of the
Danish Arts Foundation

# DANISH ARTS FOUNDATION

Cover design © Nordisk Books

Printed and bound in Great Britain by Clays Ltd, Elcograf S.p.A.

A CIP catalogue record for this book is
available from the British Library

ISBN 9780995485259

Maria Gerhardt

# Transfer Window

## Tales of the Mistakes of the Healthy

Translated by Lindy Falk van Rooyen

nordisk books

Also by Nordisk Books

*Havoc*
Tom Kristensen

*You can't betray your best friend
and learn to sing at the same time*
Kim Hiorthøy

*Love/War*
Ebba Witt-Brattström

*Zero*
Gine-Cornelia Pedersen

*Termin*
Henrik Nor-Hansen

You have to earn
Smell good
For your lover
For your parents
Not to die alone
Not to die in shame


*Amager Champion*
Maria Gerhardt, 2015

There is a place by the beach in Hellerup called Rosenhaven, where I sit when I cannot sleep. I wait for the
sun, smoking cigarettes while I wait, smoking cigarettes,
even though it's not allowed. My legs twitch. Damaged
nerves, they say. Bodily notifications. It is written in red, it
is written in yellow, it is written in orange, yours truly, stage
four. I don't know how late it is, a watch isn't allowed in here.
My bag is packed with the absolute essentials, and I have
a cord I can pull when I need help. Matches and money.
Our currency is stamped with miracles. I wait for the sun,
smoking cigarettes while I wait, smoking cigarettes, even
though it's not allowed. When I close my eyes I'm roused by
the sounds. For a startled moment I forget that doom isn't
bearing down, doom is already here.

It looks like it's burning out there, a boat, a family, one of each kind, two by two on the horizon. I pull the cord, and a kind employee appears within minutes. He puts his hand on my shoulder. "Come, let's get you home, now," he says. "There's a fire," I say. "Could it be a refugee family?" You hear about these things all the time, I wish that I could, but I'm too weak to help. He gently ushers me off the bridge. "It's just a reflection on the water," he says. "Come on now, let's get you home." I stand up slowly. I feel dizzy and I remember the kindly advice I received when I checked in last summer. Try not to have too many opinions about things, you'll get worn out so quickly.

I remember searching the internet. I remember reading up on everything, without getting involved. Algorithms and acquaintances; people wondering when I'd make some sort of statement. I scoffed at their ignorance that it was for their sake I held my tongue. Death rules in diplomacy.

We have already said goodbye to our families in a beautiful ceremony. Children danced along the boardwalk on Strand-boulevard, all dressed in white. Nuns greeted the guests at the door of the age-old chapel of Saint Joseph. The oldest of the Sisters laid a hand on my forehead. "We've always taken care of our sick," she said. "This is not new, 'tis how it's always been." Then we boarded one of the adapted Ti-voli-trains, and took a tour of the grounds. The elders waved from the balconies. There was free sushi for the newbies. At sunset you guys had to leave, I cried down my new white shirtfront, but you were cool and collected, as always. We exchanged envelopes. "I can write to you," I said. "I can always write to you."

I've been here three hundred and eighty days. I have two rooms; one, where I sleep and another as a lounge. And I have a hook for my towel by the bathing bridge. We take dips in the ocean, all year round; it's compulsory and an employee, stationed on the bridge, ticks us off our names on a list when we sputter to the surface and fumble our way to the sauna. One of the elders in the sauna was humming a tune, which I couldn't place. For the rest of the day it whirled around in my head, like a virus. It might have been an old Swedish lullaby, which you used to sing for him. It hit me that it had been more than a year, since I'd listened to music.

We get home in time for the buffet breakfast and an employee kindly guides me to my usual table. He reminds me to take my morning oil. "Would you like to have some scrambled eggs?" he asks. "They're hot off the pan, still moist and shiny." I have no appetite. "There was a boat with a family burning on the horizon today," I tell the kind man, who dims our special lamps for me. "No, it was just a reflection on the water," he says. "You can ask them to explain it in science class today, there'll be time for you to ask questions after."

Music is prohibited in here. It wakes too many feelings. "Don't listen to music on your own," they say. There is Psalm-singing on Sundays, supervised by trained personnel, ready to catch you , if you break down in a song.

We eat our meals in a large hall. I always sit at the same place, a table with the ladies from card club and my good friend Mikkel. An employee, sitting at the head of the table, ensures that the conversation doesn't become too dark. Often we talk about our childhood. I reminisce about the Eighties; Mikkel is about my age, so he usually joins in. I remember a sense of community founded upon the brilliance of our football team alone, the stem of my pride. My exaggerated self-worth. I honestly believed I'd helped them win by rooting for them in our living room, summoning the entire arsenal of my telepathic powers; balled fists, every muscle in my face clenched. My uncle arrived with a couple of guys from the club, that fine day in June when we whipped the Russians 4-2. There was a rush of revolution in our living room, and I felt a sense of self-satisfaction unparalleled before or since.

"So this is Miami," said my friend on a visit, back when we lived together on the other side of the wall, when I used to bike around with a fat smile on my face. For every convertible, I had to stop for a juice, spluttering apple/beetroot/ginger at regular intervals. I'd cycle the neighbourhood flat for hours, looking at the houses, which were usually deserted, so you could stop and stare in peace. One day, wiping the pulp from my mouth, I declared: "Wow, it must be grand to live here." You snorted: "Hah, why d'you think they work so hard?" So they can afford to spend three quarters of an hour in their big white kitchens that open onto a terrace. Mild summer evenings, stolen in the Honey Hour from eight till nine, when the heavens are streaked in pastels. And the sea is right on your doorstep, when you need to soothe your winter-worn hide, or drown.

We drove along Ryvangs Allé, and I was happy, it had been closed to traffic for so long, and now, at last, it was opened; the embassy quarters on the one side, the coastal railway on the other. Everything so beautifully landscaped and freshly painted, strutting rhododendron, a testimony to the motto in Gentofte School Auditorium: Onward, Upward. We drove fast, no red lights, the trains trundled, the busses heaved, the scent of summer still in the air. And I was happy, because for a moment I forgot that we'd been to The Big Hospital, I'd forgotten the doctor who squeezed my hand and regretted to say that it had spread.

The further I fell, the cleaner our place had to be; our books were colour-coordinated, our music was sorted, nothing depressing, please, and our bedding from Egypt was always washed and ironed. Where we'd acquired such taste, I really don't know. The terrace cane chairs were scored on an auction, likewise, the saucers with a label. Stuffed butterflies danced on display in the corner cabinet. There was not a fault to be found in our French mirrored wardrobes, and nothing but my bare toes adorned our white pigment floors. Monday mornings saw me submerged in a tub with marble lion feet, the black Moroccan soap within my reach. The only hitch was my psyche, my sickness and a sprinkle of ash from our open fireplace.

I said it to everyone: "Organise a cleaning lady." This was my hottest tip for all next of kin, who kept asking with puppy-dog eyes: "How can we help?" "Isn't there anything we can do to help?" "Come over and scrub my sink, or organise a cleaning lady," I said. Right till the day my cleaning lady said that her husband suffered from an ostomy. Till my regular doctor at The Big Hospital had a blood clot on the brain. And I, yet again, was so ill one morning that I was loath to cancel our cleaning lady. I wanted a juice, but veggies made me nauseous and the kid was tossing his toys all over the place . He coaxed ravens onto the balcony with bread and threw popcorn with a practiced hand. My sore feet trod on the corns, burning as if cut on shattered glass. I was yelling before eight in the morning. I snarled like a dog, despite the fact that he was terrified of dogs. He shimmied into the corner with a water pistol, but the ravens refused to come. You'd gone to fetch eggs, but we already had eggs on the back fridge shelf for the dying. "Bad planning and wasting food just makes my migraine worse," I yelled, as he coaxed ravens onto the balcony with bread.

Now I had to throw up and now I didn't; now I had to throw up and now I didn't. I'd made a promise to write fiction, not record yet another chaotic morning, when he aped the sound of my gagging and smacked his hand to his forehead. I caught your eye with a signal, like a coach to a referee when he wants to bring in a substitute player. Now I had to throw up and now I didn't; now I had to throw up and now I didn't, and when I finally emerged from the bathroom, the flat was quiet. Your breakfast was stood on the table, just as you had served it, untouched.

I remember a springtime with seven physicians all staring with heads cocked. My regular nurses sighed and rolled their eyes on their way down for coffee after long consultations when I just sat there crying in a cup, loath to spill more bodily fluid on the floor. I remember waiting in waiting rooms, listening to other people's social security numbers being called, furious at the post-war generation crowded around me, twitching in their wigs. What have you got to bawl about? You guys have seen the 50s, the 60s, the 70s, the 80s, the 90s, the turn of the 21st century and counting. I despise you and your grief, your awkward sons staring at me. I know I look young in my sports attire and tattoos. I could have been in my prime. I could have been happy-go-lucky, before I came through that door. I could have been singing a song on my bike; a cheesy ballad from the eighties, full blast, clean across greater Østerbro. But this place never fails to get me down; the waiting room, the stats, the stupid and the overweight, all these people who're supposed to die before I do.

I remember the white hoodie I used to wear, all splattered
with blood, primarily my own, of course. It was a bitch to
stick a needle in me. They tried and tried, tied themselves
in knots, and I told the same joke every time; what a useless
addict I'd make. They tied themselves in knots, again and
again, and they called in help, four or five times, till finally
I got a free pass up to the twelfth floor and the nurse from
Anaesthesia; the uppermost rung in the hierarchy. My blood
vessels lie very deep down, and I could never understand
why they didn't have a scanner, often I wondered if there
was someplace, where I could give blood intravenously and
spare my white hoodie from further stain; they had a similar
set up in the place where I was pumped with Vitamin-C,
listening to the talk of the other patients, which always
revolved around pills and dietary supplements. It was a bitch
to stick a needle in me. And when I went home, the needle
finally in place to be pulled out later, the blood stained again,
and I started to cry, because I had a meeting in town, and
now my sleeve was all bloody, and the kind nurse would
wrap it in duct tape, and this was me hitting the streets of
October; crying, with plasters on my clothes.

We rarely had guests – it happened less and less – in houses where the sick live; no matter how clean your home, the pall of The Big Hospital lingers. But on those few occasions, when someone popped in, he gave them a tour of our home. He showed them around the rooms and explained what we do there, in bare pleonastic terms: This is a lamp, which lights the room. This is a fireplace, where you can make fires. There is a stove, where you can boil eggs. Then he would point to the bedroom: "This is Maria's room, where she can lie down and sleep."

Those autumn seasons, when I lay in the same posture with a pillow under each arm, my eyes shut tight. Those seasons, when I did not move a muscle. I just lay there, till I had to pee, or the hunger became too great. I lay there till about three, when I fought my way out of bed to pick him up from kindergarten, or to empty the dishwasher. I cancelled all appointments, those I still had to speak of. I barely moved. I locked out all thought. I lay there like this, till you came home around five, when some kind of intimacy or another had to be mustered. I lay like this for days, for weeks, for months, and the best part of all was when I had managed to walk all the way into the kitchen, I had wrestled the remaining egg off the cutting board and, teeth chattering, had crawled back into bed, gratefully sinking into the same posture again. I was sick; it was like being a kid, who is reluctant to leave the water, even though his time was up; as long as you are asleep, all your options are still open.

There were days allocated to tears from 9:00 to circa 3:30 pm. There was so much water. I had to apply another coating of face cream after tea. The snot coursed down my face in elevens like a child; the crying in sync with how far I dared think, and the fear began to take over. The shaking was new to me, though. Usually, I could think things through to their logical conclusion, but maybe till now my body had dismissed most thoughts as silly little notions; what a lot of nonsense, ha, ha ha! But this was different. And you could see it in my eyes. My body knew pain which the body can't bear. And I found myself curled in a ball, sobbing, but still believing that someone would come and save me. For it couldn't be true that so much pain was destined, for me. I grew up breathing the air of the eighties, the age of collective communities, which believed in social justice. I was educated in a Danish state school and graduated with a first class pass in comradeship. I had spent a decade of activism on the left wing. Where had I gone wrong? Why had I, in particular, been allocated such a large plot in hell? My sweetheart, you are not to see my lying here sobbing. You are not to see me hunched over the toilet bowl, howling for help down the drain. My sweetheart, I wanted to be your best, but we had just a short season, and no matter how many walls we built, how many mattresses we piled up, the pea always made its way, mutated, sailed along the drains and sprouted in clumps of disused potential. Life is not fair; death comes into its own.

He did not want my help dressing, and he did not want my
bedtime stories, my songs, my games, and I kept telling myself
that it was okay. Even as I swore and cried when he wasn't
around. I lay awake at night, because this is what I do, lie
awake, and you could see where this was heading. I moved
to the couch in the lounge and the basket of sleeping pills
still stood on the stove when you woke the next morning. My
patently desperate attempts to find some peace; you let me
sleep, and I woke up, just as the two of you were about to
leave, after your yoga and oats porridge and books, he'd even
had a stint upstairs to play, and I got up to make a fumbling,
half-hearted attempt to help, but he didn't want my help with
his snowsuit, his gumboots, or any of the other things he
usually could do perfectly well on his own, but not that day,
that day, he refused to do anything, and I thought to myself, it's
okay, and I said so, quietly, it's okay, and you got mad, and told
him to hurry, you didn't have time for this, I hated that you said
you didn't have time. You have so much time. You have nothing
but time. "Do you want to go kindergarten in your pyjamas?"
you asked, hands on hips. And then he started to cry, so did I,
and fled to the bathroom, where I chanted, it's okay, it's okay.
I tried splashing water on my face, tried taking a bath, but the
fear kept rising, and then the nausea came, and I had to throw
up, and still you guys hadn't left, because you just needed one
last thing, before you could go, and you knocked on the door,
asked if I'd seen your phone, I whimpered that I hadn't, and
lay down on the floor by the toilet, the seat was up, which
either means that you've got a boy or a man in the house, or
someone, who throws up all the time. I closed my eyes, tried to
breathe in a particular way that is supposed to help, and I said
to myself, again and again, that it was okay; it was okay that he
didn't want me as a parent, now that I would soon be dead.

27

I remember the list, updated weekly, of friends who couldn't bear to be around me.

In here I am never alone. If I lack company, I can go onto the streets. A number of green parks have been landscaped, with various benches scattered in opportune places. People talking in hubs here, there and everywhere, for lack of social media. They play cards, or rounds of pétanque. There is a feel of Mediterranean village life. In winter, several locales on Strandvejen are decked with easy chairs and board games. Folk say *hej* as I pass by. On singular occasions an elder blocks my path with a bear hug. I'm not sure if it's orchestrated, but it works. It's a far cry from the gaping holes in day to day life beyond the wall, when everyone else was working, and I was barricaded under blankets, reduced to a statistic in the normalcy of my friends' lives and journeys and culinary experiences ad infinitum. The winters I lay scrolling, till my fingers were stiff, my body seized in the agony that only a body in absence of motion feels.

The sick are sent stacks of emojis.

I etch lines in the wall, to the left of my mattress, in order to keep track of how long I have been here. I have two rooms, and a wall covered in pictures of those I love. I have a wall covered in pictures of those I left. I had packed twenty kilos and rung for a taxi, the day I ran into an old friend, who had run into you. Actually, he'd already gone past, but lingered by the window display at Illum, his eyes following you down Købmagergade. He could barely recognise you, that's what he said, his hand on my arm, he spoke softly: "Grief has made its mark in her face."

We go for a sushi lunch outdoors on the roofed terrace. Mikkel orders his usual salmon salad. We're discussing the political policy that led to us being held here. "The welfare state was bled, till it no longer could be saved," says Mikkel. "They had to create an outlet to avoid the onset of anarchy." "Some Social Democrat probably sat thinking up a solution, whilst gazing over Stauning's Park at the sea beyond," I say. "And he thought: we've vacated palaces before, so the common folk have a place to grill their sausages, and we'll do it again!" "Maybe they drank one Schnapps too many at a Christmas party," Mikkel snorts. "You know, six pale-blue shirts at a buffet lunch, it can only end badly." Mikkel gets up from his chair, balls his right fist in the air, playing the fool: "We will make history! People will love us for this, we will ease their worst fears, wrap them in cotton wool, in a breathtaking environment." He's making a bit of a scene, and a couple of elder ladies a few tables away are gawking at him. "Good Lord, the Northern suburbs shouldn't be a reserve for rich and healthy – but the sick and dying!"

This enormous Hospice, unparalleled anywhere in the world, starts at the gateway on Strandvejen; here Saint Joseph's Institute meets the Tuborg bottle, re-painted white as a Ramlösa capped in gold, everything has been refashioned in white and blue tones. A big, white wall cuts through North Zealand. We have been granted the entire coastline from Tuborg Harbour to Bellevue Beach. The private beaches have been appropriated, the shingle removed and sand banks formed in a promenade for the length of the tract; the walk there and back takes about three-quarters of an hour. Sea kale and samphire are cultivated on the embankment and saunas dot the route. The eldest residents live in villas on the waterfront. The physicians live in the white building that Arne Jacobsen designed in the 30s. We have occupied the core of Hellerup, Charlottenlund Fort Park and the sea baths; the former Aquarium is a massive training facility for physiotherapy. Café Jorden Rundt is a 24-hour raw juice bar with recipes from around the globe. We stage our annual play in Bellevue Theatre. Bar a miraculous recovery, once you check in, you can never leave. We own the high-end restaurants. And Bakken amusement park, of course. You can win a range of expensive medical treatments at the Sommerfest Tombola. Or at the shooting range, if you prefer. You can also dart balloons and bet on horses, or ducks. We acquired Peter Liep's House restaurant and run the shortest horse-drawn cart tours in the world. The remainder of Jægersborg's forest park has been cordoned off with a double barbed wire fence. Yapping German Shepherds patrol the break in between.

I pick up Mikkel on Hambros Allé in Hellerup, where the football players used to keep their homes. I imagine these super fit, salt and pepper haired men, who can turn a million a week, making a getaway in an over-stuffed Cabriolet; their kids are screaming as they drive over the bridge, their wives are ready for divorce before they reach the outskirts of Italy. I'd messaged Mikkel, and asked if he was up for a round of tennis at ten. I've got problems with my hip, and I've taken an extra dose of oil, both will probably hamper my game. He didn't reply. Maybe he'd gone to Øregaard Park to feed the ducks, or to pet the yard animals at the Karen Blixen Museum, where they've just had a pen installed for puppies. Last I was there, I saw an old lady, who had plainly just started on cannabis oil. She drooled more than the three-week-old golden retrievers. At last Mikkel opens the doors to the stately mansion; even here, he knows someone who knows someone. We take a seat in the conservatory, and he blends in perfectly. You can see by the way he favours one leg that also he has a loss of feeling.

"Have you tried alternative treatment?" The fit and healthy have so many questions that I considered printing a little pocket book that listed everything I'd tried, and I'd make comments in the margins, noting effects and side effects, how it feels right there, how it feels, when I can't feel anything at all. Nothing but nausea. And a yearning for white bread. I remember the autumn I ingested no food. It was not a hunger strike. It was not a choice. It was not a side effect of chemo. I just couldn't hold anything down. "You must be tired," said my regular nurse. "Yup, I solve that problem by not getting up," I said. Once a week, tests were taken. Blood tests, urine tests, stool tests. In the interim, I avoided the vicinity of food. No supermarkets, no fridges, no eggs. I lay there, supine, as always wondering whether there was someone I should be calling. There must be someone. Some or other expert, some kind of miracle. Someone who knew someone. I ploughed directories and the internet from end to end, listing whatever I hadn't tried yet. I had Immuno-therapy to my credit. And Proton Radiation Therapy. I only lasted a month without milk. I hadn't tried being locked in ayurvedic asylum, where they break down your immune system, then slowly build it back up again. I only lasted a month without coffee. I had no talent for mistletoe tea. It was hard being a vegan on chemo. I hadn't checked myself into a Gerson Clinic in Mexico. I hadn't travelled to North India to consult the Dalai Lama's personal physicians, who, I am told, treat their patients orally, with silver and gold.

Somewhere in the mountains of Granada I visited the English Queen of Detox and fasted for the God-knows-how-manyth time. After a week on juice and a single stolen orange, which hadn't been squeezed, we danced in the after-noons. We were told to sway to the music and say something beautiful to one another. "You're beautiful," the librarian from Birmingham said to me, and I broke down and cried. Later, I yelled at the dance teacher, desperate, "Play some punk! Play some techno!" The Queen took stock at the end of the week. Reviewing my medical history, she began at the beginning and stared at my non-existent boobs. "Do you know what this means?" she asked me in English. "No, I don't..." I replied in kind. "It means problems with your mother."

"Did your biological father leave your family when you were a baby?" the Israeli healer asked in English, moving her hands over my belly all the while, rhythmically, from left to right. "Yeah, sort of," I replied politely, giving her a tentative smile in the hope that, apart from healing me, she would also like me. She paused to change positions, her hands now moving from right to left. "Hmm, that might have affected your cells in a destructive way."

"Are you a smoker?" the acclaimed German doctor with Asperger's asked as he jabbed a catheter into my groin, along the artery of the tumour, so the chemo could access my right lung directly. "I am a former smoker," I said, staring at the large screens, which provided an opportunity to follow the treatment's progress, should I so wish. He had a habit of speaking very loudly, right into my face, as he performed the most painful part of the procedure. In the nigh on two minutes he scorched my left lung without anaesthetic, he yelled: "I hear you're going to the Amalfi Coast to write, they have the most amazing Limoncello there!"

The boutiques along Strandvej changed after they built the Hospice. All the clothing shops are gone. No more polo shirts and black bits & bobs with fur. A few special- ise in white accessories; bags and scarves, white sneakers ad libitum. We have five different juice bars. Three shops selling healthy snacks, dark chocolate, liquorice root and date balls. They're very popular with the newbies, who don't get a proper dose of oil, just yet, and they loiter outside, lounging in cafés, till the boutiques open their doors. The photography shop has boomed. No one takes digital pictures in here, and there are so many people to miss, on the other side of the wall. There's always a queue, and the elderly owner, jogging back and forth between customers and pallets stacked with glossy photo albums, enlarges and frames pictures of grandchildren in swimming pools. There are kiosks selling newspapers, lotto slips, a modest selection of sweets and crisps we can buy with our ration of coupons. It is for your personal trainer to decide, how many coupons you get; if you bunk your training, you don't get any. Then you're left with the black market in Rosenhaven, where you can buy cigarettes and sweets with E-numbers, and I know for a fact, that Mikkel can organize booze from one of the owners. There's a deluge of masseurs, over and above the weekly sessions that everyone is entitled to; therapists of every creed. Gentofte Public Library is still up and running, but the children's section has been moved; the sick kids have their own place on the North Sea coast. In Øregård Park there's a cosy converted café, which sells the classics and new novels, providing another spot you can get a coffee and just chill. This is how I spent most of my adult life; sat in a chair, surrounded by books and cappuccino. It almost felt like the old days. Bar the computer, bar my ambitions.

After tennis I think we're going for a swim in the sea, but Mikkel has other plans. He wants to go to the Virtual Reality Store, and I know what this means. "You wait here," he says, as he puts on the apparatus. He likes to smoke during the show, and I don't know how he winged it, but for some reason, he's allowed to. He explains to the shop assistant which memories he wants to relive, and he's picked this particular scenario before, so it doesn't take long to create. Fresh memories take them longer; you have to describe the experience in detail, bring along pictures, if you like, before they can then create your story and, usually, you have to allow for a couple of adjustments, till they get it just right. Mikkel has settled into their large, leather easy chair. He doesn't have to interact. All he has to do is don the over-dimensional goggles and watch, shattered, smoking and let the ash stain his white shirt.

Visiting hours are on Sundays, when the next of kin flock to the gate and stand in a curly queue to get a glimpse of loved ones who have vanished from their daily lives. You've come twice in the space of a year. The first time, we took a tour on the converted Tivoli train. We held hands behind his back. The second time, we spent in my room. I have a bed and a desk, forty-five square metres with a view of trees. He sat down and wanted to draw. Whenever I tried to catch your eye, you looked away and I was filled with a disproportionate rage, which rises when I think of your life, outside. It's easier, if you stay away. It is easier, if he gets used to me not being around. It is easier to think it's okay that you'll love someone else one day. They fetch my laundry on Thursdays. Lunch I can eat in my room, if I want to. There aren't any locks in the Hospice, but you can put a sign on your door, if you don't want to be disturbed.

I'm thinking about my friend on the other side of the wall, about that day, sitting in a train, when we agreed to become so rich and famous that we could pay someone to perform the sole task of stretching our muscles before breakfast. We laid bets on which one of us would reach Nirvana first. I'm reminded of him Tuesday mornings, when the physiotherapist with the thin face and warm hands knocks on my door. As a rule, I refrain to ask if she thinks it'll improve. "We're keeping such a tight rein on things," as she says. After the massage I put on the white underpants, the long white slacks and my white shirt. I take my oil. I grab my towel and go down to the beach. I don't have to do anything today, other than care for my body and soul, enjoy life, as they say. There is no one to disappoint, no one to burden. Everyone, who does anything for me, is paid one-hundred-and-fifty kroner an hour. No one has to call me up voluntarily, or come for a visit and get a bad conscience about all the things they cannot change.

I remember what you said in the early years. "I'm still banking on you getting well again." And I smiled and kissed you, whenever you said it. And we made plans. For we were agreed. We should keep making plans. "You must hold onto your dreams," someone once said to me. And I said: "Yes!" I said it to everyone during those spring seasons, when beauty returned against all odds. "It's important to hold onto our dreams as a family, together." I said it to everyone, and it warmed my heart every time. Once in a while, I recovered enough to start comparing our lives with that of others. Also we were going to Los Angeles, of course we were, right till the moment the insurance company said no. Also we were going to buy a summer house, of course we were, right till the moment the bank refused to lend us any money. It was not unreasonable, after all, to be reluctant about lending cash to someone without a future.

The 33rd therapist I consulted told me to relax and search my soul. Re-watch old video cassettes recording sprints, learn them by heart; practiced dodges and strategies. I stood staring at myself in front of the mirror, and finally abandoned Michael Laudrup's smile, his teeth and his feet to adopt the pendulum woman's sun greeting to perfection instead. One particular cancer coach filled my bag with tea and rituals, and I did exactly as she said: gargle with olive oil every morning. I drank a concoction of pepper and turmeric. You could wake me in the middle of the night and quiz me on vitamins, minerals and dietary supplements. I practiced the complete silent yin-yoga. I've done the regular as well as hot flow classes. I've undergone hypnosis, consulted two acupuncturists, two reflexologists and three Body SDS masseurs. I delved into a special kind of deep friction massage, I was healed by a healer, and not a day went by on the other side of the wall, when I didn't, if only for a moment, believe that I could see that they were players; the fit and healthy. And this gave me hope. Maybe it's all just one, long protracted test of my resilience. Maybe the moment will come when they give up the game, drop whatever they're doing, point to the hidden cameras in the bushes and laughingly tell me that my life has been the world's greatest candid camera show ever recorded.

Before coming in here I used to lie in bed and correspond with other cancer patients, the toughest pen pals I'd ever had. "There must be something I've still got to learn," wrote Karen. "For it's come back again." "Hm-yeah," I wrote. "I'd be careful going down that road, it can involve so much guilt." "But I'm very keen on a holistic approach," she wrote. "It can't just come from nowhere." "Maybe it does," I wrote back. "Maybe it's completely arbitrary that we, in particular, have become ill." I can see that she never got a chance to click on the last message.

Sandra's tumour had spread. She posted a picture that clearly showed that she'd been crying. "I'm scared," she wrote. "I'm 32- years-old, I have three children, and I'm scared. My husband and I are walking round in a daze." It had spread to her heart; I didn't even know that could happen. She spent the afternoon making candles with her children. The day after, her husband posted his thanks to the group.

Louise wrote on Easter weekend, directly from the ambulance: "It's spread to my spinal tissue, it spread very quickly," followed by a smiley with a tear on its ochre cheek.

"What a life. Thanks for nothing," wrote Charlotte, before it spread to her eyes.

All those young mothers who deteriorated so fast cut me in half. Lying in bed and following their lives were the hardest novels I'd ever read. The logistics alone were staggering. There was so much stress. Could they stay in the house, would they be fired? What should they say to their children? Cancer cells seemed to mutate faster and faster in these young bodies, all their clocks wound to a halt, blaring alarms. Is it possible to revisit Hell? If yes, what kind of body lotion should you bring? And how many bedsores can the skin bear? Every time there was a new post on the group, I could see the hair on my arms rise. Breaking news.

Stine kept her hair, her husband and her job. After several sessions with a psychologist, her children were out of the woods. Her colleague turned to ask her after lunch at work: "Did it do you good to come in to work today?"

I saw as pregnant women see, mothers-to-be everywhere. The streets seemed filled with prams and bubbling joy. All is beginning. All is spring. All an A. I saw the dying. I saw the first signs of rot and ruins. I took note of endings. I read obituaries. They stuck to me, and I was starting to stink.

"Yes, we've lost four people since Christmas," Marianne says in card club today. "Cheers," I say. Not that I have a drink in my hand. "Shall we play Old Maid?" I try again. I get a couple of laughs. We've all got exactly the same diagnosis. Some in the group have been here for over five years, so they've got a slot in a villa on the beach. I shuffle the cards, glance at the ladies sitting around the table. Are my odds any better than anyone else's? Have I got a better hand? I'd rather be in a team with the bit-sized, nippy types. I tick off the names of the people present. Put a little cross by the names of the people who should have been here. How eighties can you be; pick out the friends in a circle who are going to die.

Mikkel and I pitch up on Hellerup Beach before the doctors and elder nudists get there. It's May. We're in shorts, bearing tattoos. "Look," says Mikkel. "We've got a message in a bottle." We smash the old bottle carefully against a rock, and extract the letter. I recognize the handwriting; it belongs to one of our most persistent reporters. She's been banned from the Hospice. She's tried several tricks. Pretended to be a relative, picked her way along the queue Sundays. Dishing out strips of paper with her telephone number on the back. She's also tried to check in. Everyone at the Hospice knows the story. It gets better in the hall after dinner, the disdain widespread. "Dear one of you." We're already snorting with laughter. "I had polio as a child, and I feel an urgent need to tell your story. Call me. Please allow me to record your final moments."

Once in a while the conspiracy theories run riot. I could see them huddled together. The doctors and the dons of the pharma industry. And in the middle, running some kind of obstacle course, was me. Every day, I jumped and danced and curtseyed and made a mountain of money for them. I researched the range of drugs, horrified by what a goldmine I was. A fine, cute little hamster. For chemotherapy causes nausea, nausea pills cause constipation, and laxatives give you diarrhoea. Anti-hormones give you joint pain, and joint pain medicine gives you osteoporosis. Morphine gives both nausea and constipation, and morphine is addictive. I saw pushers pocketing my money, maybe having a laugh about the thin oil they'd just palmed off on me. I transferred 1.000 kroner to the 34th therapist on MobilePay, without feeling the slightest difference in my body. When I wasn't buying, I lounged about, discussing side effects with other hamsters: "I've only lost the skin under my right foot," wrote one of them. "My lung capacity is down by 30 percent, I've got a bit of an upset stomach, oh, and I've invested in a walker. Apart from that, perfectly fine, excellent product, a double thumbs up from me."

The nuns grow their plants on the shore near Tuborg. In winter they cultivate them in the big Laboratory, which used to be Saxo Bank's HQ. The beautiful greenhouse is now a study in natural cannabis, and we cross ourselves in gratitude every time we pass. The nuns harvest from new to full moon and rest afterwards, later distributing their oils and balms on foot. Nobody knows how old the sisters' order is; they wear blue and white gold-stitched tunics and a kindly smile. The oldest of the sisters once said to me: "Some people need to extend their senses, or else they'll simply hover in some unknown place just under the skin."

Every 3rd week I go swimming with my chief physician. As a rule, I go round to her place, a building where all the doctors live in Bella Vista. She opens the door with a smile, says she'll be out in a minute. We chit-chat our way to Bellevue Beach. She goes into the water first. Scanning takes place in spring. Status reports are made only once a year. Should any deterioration have occurred, a new plan is made, your diet is changed and a doctor gives a presentation of the latest available treatments; before coming to live here, they have to confirm in writing their independence from the pharmaceutical industry. The bimonthly scans of the old days are over. A body forever in a state of emergency. All those waiting rooms filled with fear. The weekly meetings at The Big Hospital, the sustained shock in doctors' rooms with pictures on a computer showing parts of me lit on screen. I remember the first time I asked about my right hip. "I don't have it there, do I?" "Oh, yes, you do," she said. "It's pretty much moth-eaten." For weeks, I could think of nothing but this one word. Moth-eaten. The water looks lovely today. My chief physician calls to me standing on the shore. "Jump in, it's wonderfully cold."

If I want to feel something, I go to the Virtual Reality Store, and, as usual, I've asked them to show our first trip to Christiania that single, sunny day in a blanket of rain one July. I needed oil, but my local supply was dry. He wasn't happy about the free roaming dogs, but the playground had shade, and there was a kiosk selling ice-cream across the road from the supermarket. Afterwards we stole a swim at the locals' secret beach, and on our way home we took the route along Pusher Street, which was lined with police patrol cars. "Is there a war going on?" he asked. "Do ninjas live here?"

We lie about the oil. Mikkel and I. So that they'll up our dosage. Same goes for morphine. At our monthly meetings, when the nuns ask if we're in pain, I quietly shake my head. "I get a stab in my leg whenever I lie down. It gets really bad at night." The oldest nun looks at me sceptically, makes a note in her journal. "I'm going to increase your two drops to three." We're ecstatic. "Hey, I believe they're having a tasting at the Welfare Store," says Mikkel. "That's just what we need," I say. We slip out and steal a golf cart from one of the residents with advanced ambulatory impediments.

We are given such healthy food to eat. Farmers arrive with their produce from Samsø, Hven and Amager. Tuborg Harbour looks like a food market in Bangkok, every day of the week. I decide to go for a vegetable juice, I choose to sit out of the sun. This is what grown-ups do; this is how to take care of yourself. The difference is that I don't have to wash up, and I don't have to deal with the pesky pulp. A lady in her sixties with a sullen face and crutches jumps the queue. A ruckus about the lack of fresh beetroot ensues. I give her a cold stare. "Take it easy, lady," I say, "I'm just here for the sugar."

Lili has been here the longest, and I've always been fascinated by hierarchies, so I hang out in her palace at Sundvænget; this is where the elders stay. I offer her my hand at the front door, and give her a hug, enquire about little things, and she responds with pictures and floral statements, life is for the living and all that jazz. Lili is the one who told me to eat my favourite meal every day of the week. She gave me a book on the power of now. I haven't read it, but whenever she asks, I express enormous enthusiasm for the theses inside. I always lay it on thick for my friends; that's how they stick around. "I'd love to come to a sermon in your church, Lili," I say. "I'd love to come to a funeral in your church, Lili," I say. "D'you reckon my Sunday will be sold out?" She swats me on the head and gives me a cookie. "Check out this cream, Lili, I ordered it from France, just for you, it's got hormones in it." She thanks me, and invites me in. I have abundant experience in making myself loved just enough to make people miss me, the day I stop buttering them up.

Just imagine if I proved to be a miracle. Just imagine if it vanished one day, and the doctors, wide-eyed, would need to sit down and study the x-rays more closely. They would send them to their peers and colleagues overseas and the tabloids would get wind of the story. Just imagine I proved to be a miracle, and my face subsequently graced the back of our fifty kroner notes in the Hospice. Just imagine if I proved to be a miracle, which showed the impossible to be possible, and my bestseller of a book, explaining exactly what I'd done, became an enchanted beacon for years to come, reminding me of the early days, when all I could think was that if the nation were to crumble, I'd be obliged to sell my story. Just imagine if I proved to be a miracle, if I were invited to sit in auditoriums world-wide, a microphone tucked in under my T-shirt before an audience that had paid an entrance fee. Just imagine if I proved to be a miracle, one of those people the fit and healthy would queue to get close to.

Mikkel has it in his stomach. We're drinking green tea with our morning oil, when we come to the conclusion that we're not into reincarnation. How's that supposed to work, then? Nobody wants to be a rat or a dog. "There must be some kind of hierarchy involved," I say. "But I, for one, don't want to end up at the bottom of the sea. I've got greater ambitions than being fish or a crab." "But that's exactly how everyone thinks, nowadays," says Mikkel. "The people we know on the other side of the wall regard themselves as some kind of royalty. They feel entitled to live 100 years, in first class. Anything less would be a catastrophe. No one lives on a busy road any more, or watches regular TV, they barely have to suffer a bad meal. Their restaurants are as thoroughly researched as their holidays. Nobody has to clock in at eight o' clock sharp, or, God forbid, any earlier. They can work from Beirut, or reclined in their beds." "Yes," I say. "Their lives are so rock solid, the apocalypse has become a sophisticated topic for dinner-party conversation, something they almost wish for, at least then they could rely on something happening. I've been there myself," I say. "Sipping lemon tea, a toothpick dipped in tar like a latter day kid pirate. Mornings on my terrace in the reserve, heavy silver strung in my torn earlobes, surrounded by roses that have more history than I do." "Not the worst place to end up," says Mikkel. "No," I say, "if only I hadn't been mesmerized by a painted cranium under the neon-light of the Anjuna night market in Goa. If only I hadn't insisted on tattoos like the boys of my generation; anchor, pocket-watch, pistol and naked dame. First batch bubble-wrap children; no suicide, no starvation. Forever vying for the least painful life, yet determined to look like you've been in a war, or at least sailed the seas." "Yes," says Mikkel. "A blackjack, Mexican style, a skull with Mickey Mouse ears, as if death was invented by Disney."

"Unpredictability is the font of survival," says my favourite teacher, a mature Norwegian woman, who habitually sashays into her fully-booked class, which is held in the loft of Rotunden Café. Her science courses are a cross between university and night school. Catalogues for courses come twice a year, and are also free of charge, like our yoga and mindfulness sessions. "See the butterfly," she says, setting a lemon specimen free before the motley flock of her class. "See how arbitrarily it flies. Random walks!" she practically yells. "Unpredictability is wired into its DNA, there is no recognizable pattern that the enemy can spy."

The 1st of each month we receive 5.000 kroner; a kind of citizens' salary or pocket money. Many convert the currency and send it to their families. Some people save; you can apply for travel, but it takes time to get leave. Some people spend every penny they have on cigarettes and cola on the black market. The accommodation is split into male and female quarters, which makes us a popular location for immigrant residents. White hijabs are available for purchase at Strandvejen No. 121. Many have asked why North Zealand, in particular, was chosen for the purposes of our Hospice. There's an ongoing court battle between the state and a group of former residents who cannot comprehend why they've been bumped from one of the most beautiful coastlines in the world. But our coastline is so white, so chaste and clean, such a natural choice to change the course of history.

The most money by far I spend in the Virtual Reality Store. That summer's day we got caught in a cloudburst, sitting in a marquee at your parents' place on Møn, there was nothing to do but wait out the storm, and we could see the horizon move, as we drank Nordic Light with leftover fried onions from a big buffet. He was so exhausted from exploring his own forest battlefield all day that he fell asleep in my lap. I've asked them to extend the last part. I'm sitting in the chair on Strandvejen, wearing oversize goggles. I'm sitting in the marquee on Møn, listening to him snore in a loop. The sheer joy in still being a haven of trust, so big and strong you can curl up and fall asleep on top of me.

I startle out of a recurring dream in a sweat. It's fashion week in Copenhagen, I've been given a clean bill of health and a vote of confidence, rising in value. Everyone is calling me up again. I'm on stage, playing my music. A guy comes up onto the stage and he wants to talk. I give him my hand. Raise my glass in a toast. He's sweating, and his eyes are on fire. I'm wearing headphones, one ear is covered, the other free, and he seeks out the latter. "My mom's cancer also started in her breasts." "Okay," I say, trying to ward him off gently but firmly with the edge of my hip. "But then it spread." His pupils are big as saucers. I don't dare look him in the eye, I look down and mix my next number. "She fought bravely for five years." I cover my free ear. I signal a guard; this guy needs to go. "She was sick for many years," he yells up at me, as the guards haul him off the stage. "She was sick for many, many years." They've managed to get him down, he claws onto arbitrary bystanders on the door floor. "I was just a little boy, when she died."

We sit and stare at each other in terror at card club today. There's an outspread lack of focus. An ever present fear that it has penetrated the brain.

This really is a ghastly place to be. Half dead and half alive.
It's not surprising that people duck; my thrashing wings,
such a horrid flailing in and out of every world. You have
one of two possibilities: to rise from the ashes, and run a
marathon. The self-healing human being. Or, you can be
a tragedy. My mother will lose me again. This time for
good. My son will call for me in his sleep. My friends don't
know when to light their candles. Do we look into or out
of a transfer window? The bane of always having to be so
existential when you'd rather be talking about so-and-so's
screwed-up love life.

I ask them to run the jittery slide show of the young man who danced for her, in nothing but his underpants, a hospital shirt and a colourful scarf wrapped round his head. We hadn't slept in a week. It had been hard for the people in the store to capture the atmosphere. "Imagine a handful of kids on a raft, who will only come in to land once fresh provisions have arrived," I tried to explain. On his shirt, in bold blue letters: Property of Copenhagen Hospital Laundry. He danced to Happy Mondays. He danced to my youth. He danced in the unending evenings on Finsensvej. He danced in the unending mornings on Finsensvej. Back in the days when he tried to attract her attention. Back in the days when all of us did.

It's like standing on the pavement outside Tivoli, hearing the people on the roller coasters scream, said an acquaintance I bumped into in front of the Glyptotek Gallery. "Life goes up and down," she said. "Yes," I said, dabbing the drops of theatre-blood off my nostrils, jumping at the whoosh of a bus. I think of her whenever I'm waiting at that crossroads, the good-time-girl who disappeared; chiselled in marble, cut in cocaine, or a peculiar stuff coming from I don't know where. "Jeez, have you brought all your problems along?" she asked one night we were out at Rio Bravo for all-you-can -eat roast pork. "Why don't we share a gram, so it all goes away?" "No, thanks," I said. "It's Tuesday." "Exactly," she said, signalling the waiter for the bill.

Once a year we're given leave to get drunk with a person of choice from our past. The yacht club is filled with balloons and place cards. We've drawn straws to decide whose favourite song is played when. My best loved employee is sitting at the head of our table. I've invited the good-time-girl, even though you thought I was being ridiculous, but you said I could, long before I came here; the dying can do all the dumb things they please. Mikkel wondered why I wanted her, of all people, to dress up and come in here a fine day in August. "Why not invite some tight young thing?" he asked, reminding me of how we lingered after breakfast, watching the canteen girls scramble our eggs to perfection, served with a smile. How do you start such a conversation? "Thanks for the eggs, yup, you've probably seen me before, that's right, table sixteen, I was the one they carried out on a stretcher last April, yeah, all better now, thanks, how about you? So, what do you do with your time, when you're not in here?" "We're patients, Mikkel," I say. "You don't go home and fuck a person who's coming apart at the seams." The girl who was invited to come, and promised to be there, doesn't come to the party. I sit watching the crowd for the rest of the evening. Mikkel is dancing to Biggie Smalls with one of the girls he met skating in the Park in the 90s; he scores a good-night-kiss and another rum cola.

At first my body wasn't destroyed, I can remember being fit on my feet in spring, crisp. When I look at the young girls in the canteen it isn't them I want; it's their bodies, which aren't destroyed, which I want, so I can destroy them.

The patients who are literally dying have rooms on the shore, in one of those refurbished buildings at the tip of Tuborg Harbour. Large windows at the foot of their beds afford a view of Øresund Sound and, first thing in the morning, the nuns open the curtains; sunrise from floor to floor. Their next of kin arrive by boat. The nuns meet them on the quay, in a sequence of preliminary rituals: First, they bathe in the sea and don the white garbs, which all of us wear. A special room is designated to the writing of last words. I'm told that your nose gets longer just before you die, that your face becomes bloated, that you drift in and out of sleep. Instead of the standard morphine trip, we also have the option of psilocybin. The nuns have beautiful stories to tell. I have already written mine: It's a morning in December when the sky has a crescendo of multi-colours. My family has gathered in soft velvet chairs, all has been said. Just before the sun breaks the horizon, the sky is lilac, and I breathe my last breath as the room turns from rose to pink, transported to the temples of Jaipur with a train of elephants. The Pink City. Here the women have rings in their noses and necklaces towering to their ears. In India the dead are sent adrift on a river; burning, their families standing on the banks, singing.

We're attending one of the biannual funeral and coffin trade fairs. Mikkel thinks it's a blast, I'm less enthusiastic. He's bought a shiny-black coffin with red trimmings. Lit de parade for an entire day with elephant beer on tap. Neil Young and *The Needle and the Damage Done* playing at the exit. Everything is settled. He's also written a will; a record collection of considerable value, a spacious flat in the centre of Copenhagen. The fairs are usually held in the hall where we eat our meals; they take up almost the entire space. There is a stand demonstrating sophisticated hologram systems, which allow you to attend your own funeral, in a manner of speaking. You can also record a short speech beforehand, which is then played in church on the day of the sermon. Mikkel is very keen on the idea. There are quite a number of Japanese exhibitors, too. The Japanese are experts in the funeral field. Many people die in Japan. Tsunami. Atomic leaks. Suicide. They know what they're doing. Alternatively, you can buy a funeral package on Amazon.com. And the Ghanaian stand does theme coffins; if you were a fisherman, you can get buried in a giant fish. Over-sized Coca-Cola bottles and hang glider coffins are additional options. Mikkel settles into an oak coffin that is whittled into a gigantic Nike trainer, crossing his hands over his chest. I don't think it's funny. "Why don't we go for a swim," I say. He ignores me. "How do you like the expression of my face when I adopt this attitude?" A salesperson comes over. "How you guys doing? I see you've found yourself a comfy spot." He and Mikkel strike up a conversation; Mikkel is still lying in the coffin. I leave the stand, I leave the hall, and I keep walking. I know that I want them to play Nick Cave, *Into My Arms*. I've done a sketch of the flower arrangements; I have sent you a draft, but you haven't replied.

It would suit me incredibly well to grow old. My medium-length, greying hair is swept back in a wave, and my suits are all tailor-made. I wear long suede boots and expensive coats in genuine wool. I take an interest in birds. A small pair of binoculars is permanently slung around my neck and a telescope is stationed on the first floor of the house we had built on a Swedish forest lake in our youth. I work upstairs in a loft, which you designed for me. It has large windows with a view of the lake and a desk, where I've written at least four or five books. We planted the rosebush the first summer after the house was completed. It reaches all the way up to the first floor now, and we have to get it trimmed every year. I have a wine cellar, grandchildren, a pension and retirement benefits, three months in the sun during the winter, and I still complain about cyclists on the pavement. I would go on package tours, peel apples on public benches, feature in a famous pop song and watch films before lunchtime, and you prove me right in the end by staying as beautiful as you've always been.

The beauty of the fact that you can never find anyone to replace me. The beauty of the fact that you do.

I would have made such an excellent patron. Every year when April comes around, I dish out generous grants from a fund in my name. The submissions I read with a hot tea and a red pen; the deadline is the 1st of November and I spend my winters reading in the usual place in Morocco. I'm so gifted at finding new talents, nudging them on; I poke and prod them on the shoulder, load their guns, Kill Your Idols. I have assistants that would do anything to beat the master. I would have made such an excellent patron, supporting the youth and saving the sick. But it is me they're collecting money for. My friends have made the rounds with a pan. My face is printed below a bank account number. My body is dependent on the money of others.

My friends were agreed when we met in a café for a coffee. Two cups and how are you, fine, and how are you. These awkward conversations, taking heed not to be too negative, avoiding the bitter invalid at all costs; the droop at the corners of her mouth, a miscreant, leech-like insect that sucks every ounce of joy out of her surroundings. These awkward conversations when everyone is aware how skewed it all is, make pains to down-play their depressions and preg- nancies. These awkward conversations ending on the note "Hey, anything can happen, right?" And I sit there, after they've gone, wondering what this means. "We could all be hit by a bus one day." "Yup, that's true." Their disappointed eyes when my mood takes a turn for the worse, even though they'd taken me out swimming and filled me with juice. "But you were in such good spirits in the summer."

Naturally I was determined to make something out of myself, and I started watching series about royal families and millionaires, documentaries on the great chefs of this world. I re-played our football-fairytale of the 80s. The victory at the Euros in 1992. I watched clips from the Olsen Gang movies; the one with the woman and the drum and the whistle and her bare toes. I re-lived Obama's road to the White House and shed a tear. And I was happy, for just as long as the programs lasted. As the credits rolled, the joy withdrew and that old, familiar feeling returned. I considered buying a lottery ticket. Taxes for stupid people, you used to quip in English. I didn't care. The last couple of years, I had often fantasised about an eternal hammock, a snip from a scene. Delightful memories of a summer on my balcony, back when I felt larger than life, one morning after yoga, downward facing dog; eastward, so also the Chinese could see me through their lenses. I turned to face Mecca and toadied to the Russians wearing Vetement socks bearing a hammer and shield. I donned my sunglasses, a white sweatband and a terrycloth robe. I folded my hands and bowed down ever so slightly, meet your new leader, Big In Japan.

Soon they'll be selling T-shirts with my name printed on the front, but still call me a loser.

We are spying through Mikkel's binoculars. From various points in the Hospice, we can follow the lives of the fit and healthy. We like watching how busy they are. "Any drama outside the supermarket today?" I ask. "No," says Mikkel. "Just some guy who's taken all of five minutes to check his receipt." "What about the bus stop?" "Nope, nothing there, either. Just five people checking their phones." "Check out this woman," says Mikkel. He passed me the binoculars, pointing. "You can see it in her posture, her drooping shoulders. She doesn't have the stuff to be happy."

From the top floor of the rehabilitation centre on the corner of Strandvejen and Strandøre we can follow our favourite couple. Mikkel isn't going to get his hip exercises done today, he's too distracted. "They're arguing, loudly," he says. "The teacups are rattling off the kitchen shelves." "Let me see," I say, deserting the rowing machine. He passes me the binoculars and points down to a yellow-brick house. I can see that the woman has sat down in a chair, her face buried in her hands. The man has walked out the door; with the naked eye, we both watch his car start and speed away. "That's what happens," says Mikkel, "when one person in a relationship becomes seriously ill: you stop arguing, and you stop fucking." I look up, lowering my binoculars. I know that his girlfriend left him when he got sick the second time. "We didn't stop fucking," I said quietly. Mikkel walks back to the exercise machine, picks up his exercise plan. "You know, sometimes I don't understand why you're in here at all," he says, trying to extend his right leg.

I'd always been brutally honest about my grotesque need for attention. My compulsive need to communicate. I had to restrain myself, not to share the thought with others, to make do with telling you instead. All our little secrets, which were the envy of the world. This is a pleasure I no longer have: An almost telepathic understanding between us, not having to say anything at all. Evenings filled with red wine, when a great deal was said. Times I merely pointed at a picture. Mornings I woke up to a book on my bedside table. Nothing has ever come close to this. And it's starting to hurt. It gnaws at my body, deeper than the pain for which I get prescribed drugs in significant doses.

I have so many letters in my drawer that I haven't managed to send. They just lie there, with your name on. I simply disappeared to here, after all. I didn't run. I just vanished. You said so yourself. "You're slipping away from me." I wanted to spare you from witnessing any further destruction. Of my body, of memories, of the person I used to be. The person I will never be again. I didn't want him to come home from school, a football tucked under his arm, only to be greeted by a large party from the palliative team. I didn't want you to see me constantly hunched over, limping, with crutches, with a walker. I didn't want you to push me around in the wheelchair I would need one day. That constant shame of being the mum on the sofa, the girlfriend from hell. I remember something he said to a girl from playgroup, when I was still able to pick him up. "My mum's got the worst sickness in the world. You can die from it. She walks round in her underpants all day."

If only we could have a bath together one more time. Get dressed, giggle our way out the garden gate and slide into the back seat of a taxi waiting on the curb, we're driven to a concert by the waterfront, and escorted to our seats on the balcony. You kiss me in the garden. You kiss me in the taxi. You are the one who taught me all about opera.

There is a place in Rosenhaven where a great deal of wheeling and stealing goes on. I like to sit here and smoke. I sit here, smoking cigarettes, even though it's not allowed. It looks like the world of yore. It smells like the world of yore. It feels good, and this makes me sad. It reminds me of those August months, when I simply was in a state of shock, rather than hemmed in. Those August months, when it was still possible to write: "Hi beautiful, gone to the beach to see the sunrise, I'll nip into the bakery for some bread on my way home."

I heard that song again. It was coming from the sauna; I think it was Lili singing. And everything welled up, all the feelings, and longing. Lying in bed together, reading aloud from the kids' newspaper. The way he burrows himself in between us, the long, communal hugs, the long communal baths. Weekends of breakfast in bed, Lego in bed, fire in the fireplace. At some point mid-morning, we'd get up and dance till one of us keeled over, exhausted.

I can't face any more white. I don't want to ask for more whites. No more hospital shirts, size medium or large. No more clogs or sandals or Stan Smiths. No more light stripes or processed dry bread. I'm going to the other side. The place that scares you. Amid the mild, planetary melodies. I'm going to soar with eagles. I'm going to soar with Grandad. I'm moving on, I'll meet new friends and there won't be a worry in the world. No walls. No wake up calls. There won't be an ego. The only thing I find frustrating about the next dimension is that you are not coming along.

I wake up one morning, and know that I'm leaving. This is my day five hundred, and it's going to be my last. I pull on an old T-shirt that I found on the beach; it is green, torn and I'm not sure why, but I took it home with me. I put it into my personal drawer, the one that the cleaning staff can't open. The drawer also contains a pair of garden shears, which I stole from Rosenhaven the day I helped to trim the roses last summer. I wear the green shirt under today's white one. I leave a letter for Mikkel in my room. I walk down the road, greet some members of the card club milling around outside. "Are you coming along to hot yoga? They've got a new instructor in from Vesterbro." "Thanks, but no thanks," I say with a wave. "Have a good time." I fantasise about fleeing across the sea at a swim, but the scenario is so banal, as if I'd read it someplace, or seen one jail-break film after another; if I'd been in better shape, I might have made it to Amager beach in an hour. I could have returned home and lived off the land.

I'm running in the break between the double fences of Jægersborg. The German Shepherds are in pursuit, and one of them latches onto my arm, but I can't feel anything. Both shirts are ripped, and I can't feel anything. Suddenly, I can't hear the dogs anymore, but I do hear a car driving by with the radio on. I must be on the other side of the wall. I stand outside a large supermarket. I must look like a homeless person, for a man comes up to me and puts a coin in my hand. I snatch it to my chest, horrified. I don't want to come home empty-handed. Soya milk, bananas, honey. We always need those. I stand in the queue, and when my items have been scanned the tired shop assistant looks up in confusion, and I realize that I'm trying to pay her with a miracle.